About the Author

Trisha Caress is a beautiful hardworking mother who has always enjoyed putting her words to paper be it nonfiction or fiction books. Trisha puts her heart and soul into everything she does, and her heart and soul are in this book. This book was written through lockdown. Trisha's always a proud black woman, but pushed forward when influenced by the Black Lives Matter movement.

I Am Black

Trisha Caress

I Am Black

Olympia Publishers
London

www.olympiapublishers.com
OLYMPIA PAPERBACK EDITION

A CIP catalogue record for this title is
available from the British Library.

ISBN: 978-1-80074-056-3

This is a work of fiction.
Names, characters, places and incidents originate from the writer's
imagination. Any resemblance to actual persons, living or dead, is
purely coincidental.

First Published in 2022

Olympia Publishers
Tallis House
2 Tallis Street
London
EC4Y 0AB

Printed in Great Britain

Dedication

This book is dedicated to my beautiful mum.

I AM BLACK

I AM BLACK
Brought here to fight your wars, yet we were still
segregated.
I AM BLACK
After World War One you sent me back, only a lucky
few were able to stay.
I AM BLACK
World War Two we were told to come to help rebuild
England,
To work as nurses,
Factory workers and other public jobs,
But still we were treated as second-class citizens.
I AM BLACK
You shot in the wrong house and killed ME.
I AM BLACK
You have shot and killed MY child.

I AM BLACK
Why is this going on today? It's 2021

I AM BLACK

I AM BLACK
You used me as a test dummy.
I AM BLACK
You burned down my churches.
I AM BLACK
You threw me to the ground.
I AM BLACK
I couldn't and still cannot even walk down the street as I am not safe.
I AM BLACK
You arrested me.
I AM BLACK
You didn't care that I was innocent.
I AM BLACK
A phone call saying that I am black is enough for you to up and shoot me.
I AM BLACK
You knelt on my neck, and killed me.

I AM BLACK
Cowards behind caps and gowns.

I AM BLACK

I AM BLACK
You left my charred body hanging from a tree.
I AM BLACK
You hid behind a white gown and cap to kill me.
I AM BLACK
You ran me over in your vehicle to kill me.
I AM BLACK
My colour offended you.
I AM BLACK
But you need me.
I AM BLACK
You put a bag over my head and killed me.

I AM BLACK

I AM BLACK
You put a burning cross in my yard.
I AM BLACK
I was intended to be this way.
I AM BLACK
I was a high priestess.
I AM BLACK
And I was the chosen one.
 I AM BLACK
God wanted me this way.
I AM BLACK
You made that a problem.
I AM BLACK
But God knew I was strong.

I AM BLACK

You stole our inventions.
Black inventors you didn't know about.

ENLIGHTEN ME
LEWIS LATIMER -1848-1928
INVENTOR AND DRAFTSMAN
Major Developments: Carbon Filament

CALL ME
DR. SHIRLEY JACKSON – 1946–PRESENT
THEORETICAL PHYSICIST
Major Developments: Touch-Tone Telephone And Caller Id

BEAT IN ME
OTIS BOYKIN – 1920-1982
INVENTOR
Major Developments: Ibm Computer, Pacemaker

WATCH ME
MARIE BAN BRITTAN BROWN – 1922-1999
INVENTOR
Major Developments: Closed-Circuit Television Security

BELIEVE IN ME
MARIAN R. COOK
SVP, AT&T LABS
Major Developments: Voip

READ ME
PHILIP EMEAGWALIE – 1954-PRESENT
SCIENTIST
Major Developments: World's Fastest Computer

WEAR ME
MARY AND MILDRED DAVIDSON
INVENTORS
Major Developments: The Sanitary Belt, Walker, Tissue Holder

FEEL ME
GARRETT MORGAN – 1877-1963
INVENTOR
Major Developments: Gas Mask, Traffic Signal

TRUST IN ME
ELIJAH MCCOY – 1843-1929
INVENTOR
Major Developments: Lubricators That Revolutionised Steam Engines And Railroad Industry

I AM BLACK

I AM BLACK
You stole me from my country.
I AM BLACK
You stole my land.
I AM BLACK
You stole me from my Mother.
I AM BLACK
You stole me from my Father.
I AM BLACK
You stole my gold.
I AM BLACK
You stole my birth rights.

I AM BLACK
Give us all our rights, all over the world.

I AM BLACK

I AM BLACK
You stole my soul.
I AM BLACK
You stole our GOD, our JESUS, and our COLOUR.
I AM BLACK
You stole my novels.
I AM BLACK
You stole my wild life.

Waiting for the Slave Ship.

I AM BLACK

I AM BLACK
You stole my freedom.
I AM BLACK
You stole me from my mother's arms.
I AM BLACK
You stole, I have a dream.

I AM BLACK

I AM BLACK
You stole my music.
I AM BLACK
You stole my ideas.
I AM BLACK
You stole my legacy.
I AM BLACK
You took away my books.
I AM BLACK
You stole my livelihood.

I AM BLACK

I AM BLACK
You tore apart my jungle.
I AM BLACK
You hunted me, like an animal.
I AM BLACK
You made me pick cotton.
I AM BLACK.
You took away my existence.
I AM BLACK
You made my blackness unworthy.
I AM BLACK
You made my blackness seem worthless.
I AM BLACK
You put me in the chains.
I AM BLACK
You sold me to the highest bidder.

Slaves Being Sold at an Auction in Richmond, Virginia, 1856

I AM BLACK

I AM BLACK
You hung me from a noose on a tree.
I AM BLACK
You cut my limbs off so I couldn't run away.
I AM BLACK
You fed me your scraps.
I AM BLACK
You raped me.
I AM BLACK
I had your children.
I AM BLACK
You whipped me.

I AM BLACK
You dragged me from the back of a truck, until I was
unrecognisable

I AM BLACK

I AM BLACK
You scarred my back with chains and anything you
could find.
I AM BLACK
I never showed you my tears.
I AM BLACK
You enjoyed watching me in the pain that you had
inflicted on me.
I AM BLACK
I tried not to show you my weakness.
I AM BLACK
You made me weak.
I AM BLACK
I built those buildings you now reside in.
I AM BLACK
You will not let me progress.

I AM BLACK
I had to pick cotton to eat.

I AM BLACK

I AM BLACK
You spat in my face.
I AM BLACK
You let me raise your children, yet you think I am
beneath you.
I AM BLACK
You made me live in a shack.
I AM BLACK
You made me work in your fields.
I AM BLACK
You made me enrich your land.
I AM BLACK
You treated your animals better than me.
I AM BLACK
You beat me for a confession for something I didn't do.
I AM BLACK
You make me feel unsafe in my own country, my home,
my neighbourhood.

I AM BLACK

I AM BLACK
Why did you think I was beneath you?
I AM BLACK
You put me in prison for years
Not because I am guilty but because I am black.
I AM BLACK
You called the police on me for sitting in my car.
I AM BLACK
If we can't live free, then what's the point in living?
I AM BLACK
You tased me several times although I was in handcuffs.
I AM BLACK
You keep telling us to go back home, I am home.
I AM BLACK
Death smiles at us all; all we need to do is smile back.

I AM BLACK

I AM BLACK
I live and breathe the same air as you.
I AM BLACK
You made me make your grand garments.
I AM BLACK
You made me wear rags.
I AM BLACK
Your feet were covered.
I AM BLACK
My feet were bare blistered and torn.
I AM BLACK
You can't call me anything racist anymore
Because I will retaliate.

I AM BLACK
The pain I endured will always be with me.

I AM BLACK

I AM BLACK
I was sick and left to die.
I AM BLACK
Yet I still cooked your meals.
I AM BLACK
You made me entertain your guests.
I AM BLACK
You made me work for nothing.
I AM BLACK
You blackened your faces to entertain others.
I AM BLACK
You asked me to come from my homeland to help build
your country,
And then many years later you sent me back, leaving
my family behind.
I AM BLACK
You didn't want me in your neighbourhood.

I AM BLACK
Why were you blackening your face to act for me?

I AM BLACK

I AM BLACK
My story wasn't told.
I AM BLACK
I have a name and it is not nigger.
I AM BLACK
I do have a place in this world.
I AM BLACK
I never understood why you hated me, just because of
my skin colour.
I AM BLACK
I served your guests.

I AM BLACK
Why, just why did you treat us this way?

I AM BLACK

I AM BLACK
I have to learn twice as hard.
I AM BLACK
I have to work twice as hard to get the same recognition
as others.
I AM BLACK
You taught your children to hate me.
I AM BLACK
I am a footballer you chanted monkey noises at.
I AM BLACK
I am a gymnast and you took away my crown, I wasn't
graceful enough.
I AM BLACK
I took a peaceful knee.

I AM BLACK
You took away my livelihood because of my peaceful
protest.

I AM BLACK

I AM BLACK
You wore white cloaks and hoods to burn me on a cross.
I AM BLACK
You were cowards hiding behind your white cloaks and
hoods.
I AM BLACK
I exist for whom I am, not my colour.
I AM BLACK
I am sad, not because I am black but because
My blackness created hatred; other nations compare me
to wild animals,
I AM NOT.
I AM BLACK
I was created this way, stolen from my home so you
could beat me, I
Was stolen so you could make me your slave.
I AM BLACK
So you whipped me.

I AM BLACK
You treated me like an animal.

I AM BLACK

I AM BLACK
So you raped me.
I AM BLACK
So you hung me.
I AM BLACK
So my hands and feet were amputated.
I AM BLACK
So you starved me.
I AM BLACK
You put me in chains.
I AM BLACK
You impregnated me, then left our children fatherless.
I AM BLACK
I bore your child.

I AM BLACK
You stood and watched, like this was normal.

I AM BLACK

I AM BLACK
You never saw my tears, when you beat me.
I AM BLACK
I was in pain.
I AM BLACK
You hated my hair and my hairstyles.
I AM BLACK
Yet you now take them for your own as if you created
them.
I AM BLACK
You hated my lips.
I AM BLACK
You now plump up your lips to be like mine.
I AM BLACK
You hated the shape of my body.
I AM BLACK
You now want my shape.

I AM BLACK

I AM BLACK
You hated the way I look.
I AM BLACK
You want to look like me.
I AM BLACK
You lay in the sunshine to darken like me.
I AM BLACK
My green is as rich as yours.
I AM BLACK
I am still fighting your wars but yet some don't see me
as equal.

I AM BLACK

I AM BLACK
Police brutality towards people of colour is still rife,
why?
I AM BLACK
Why am I burying my child because he went for a jog?
I AM BLACK
I cannot even pray in my own church in peace,
Afraid you will shoot me and my people.
I AM BLACK
You wore and still wear swastikas to intimidate all
races.
I AM BLACK
I wasn't able to have a burial, as I was never found.
I AM BLACK
Why am I always guilty until proven innocent?

I AM BLACK

Breonna Taylor, a 26-year-old African-American emergency medical technician, was fatally shot by Louisville Metro Police Department (LMPD) officers Jonathan Mattingly, Brett Hankison, and Myles Cosgrove on March 13, 2020.

I AM BLACK

I AM BLACK
Why do you ask me if "I'm looking for someone"?
Rather than "Hi, how can I help?" like I shouldn't be there.
I AM BLACK

<u>And I am proud</u>

I AM BLACK — YES I AM

I AM BLACK
Yes I am
I can read a book.
I AM BLACK
Yes I am
You can no longer beat me.
I AM BLACK
Yes I am
I am no different from you.
I AM BLACK
Yes I am
Look beyond my skin colour.
I AM BLACK
Yes I am
I will no longer wallow in pity for the way you treated
me.
I AM BLACK
Yes I am
I will eat a feast, not your scraps
I AM BLACK
Yes I am
I now own my own home.

I AM BLACK — YES I AM

I AM BLACK
Yes I am
Yes this is my property.
I AM BLACK
Yes I am
I will come and work on your railroads if I choose to.
I AM BLACK
Yes I am,
you can no longer make me pick cotton.
I AM BLACK
Yes I am,
and you can no longer.
I AM BLACK
Yes I am
I will speak freely.
I AM BLACK
Yes I am
I know you can see me.

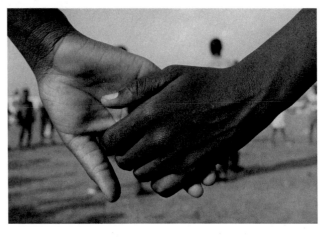

I AM BLACK — YES I AM

I AM BLACK
Yes I am
I will tell my story.
I AM BLACK
Yes I am
Stop spreading your hate towards your children;
children are not born racist.
I AM BLACK
Yes I am
I will take a peaceful knee without repercussions.
I AM BLACK
Yes I am
You will no longer offend me with your monkey noises.
I AM BLACK
Yes I am
You still do not want me in your neighbourhoods, but I
am here to stay.

I AM BLACK — YES I AM

I AM BLACK
Yes I am
I can now sit where I choose to on the bus.
I AM BLACK
Yes I am
I AM BLACK
Yes I am
I will choose who fathers my child; you cannot take me
as your property.
I AM BLACK
Yes I am
You can no longer steal my dreams.
I AM BLACK
Yes I am
Those buildings we built, we will now take credit for.

I AM BLACK — YES I AM

I AM BLACK
Yes I am
I will drink out of any fountain.
I AM BLACK
Yes I am
I will drive anywhere I desire, freely.
I AM BLACK
Yes I am
I am keeping my limbs; they are not yours to take.
I AM BLACK
Yes I am
I will get the education, that I am entitled to.
I AM BLACK
Yes I am
My history will be told.

I AM BLACK — YES I AM

I AM BLACK
Yes I am
I will never receive your spit in my face again.
I AM BLACK
Yes I am
I will no longer wear rags, I will wear fine garments.
I AM BLACK
Yes I am
I can now grieve for my mother and father openly.
I AM BLACK
Yes I am
I will rule my own kingdom.
I AM BLACK
Yes I am
My features you now want.

I AM BLACK — YES I AM

I AM BLACK
Yes I am
I am free.
I AM BLACK
Yes I am
You will pay me the same due as everyone else.
I AM BLACK
Yes I am
I will get the recognition for my inventions.
I AM BLACK
Yes I am
You will never throw stones and rocks at me again.
I AM BLACK
Yes I am.

I AM BLACK — YES I AM

I AM BLACK
Yes I am
I will now wear my crown.
I AM BLACK
Yes I am
You will never put a noose around my neck and hang
me.
I AM BLACK
Yes I am
I can act myself, there's no need to blacken your faces.
I AM BLACK
Yes I am
I can put down my own music from my own label; it
was never yours to steal.
I AM BLACK
Yes I am
I will continue to build up the world we live in, but you
will now have to pay me.

I AM BLACK
Just look, how does this make
you feel?

I AM BLACK — YES I AM

I AM BLACK
Yes I am
I am taking my land back.
I AM BLACK
Yes I am
I am getting back up after all the years I have been put
down.
I AM BLACK
Yes I am
I am no longer a slave.
I AM BLACK
Yes I am
Finally I have my smile back.
I AM BLACK
Yes I am
You can no longer take your whip to my back.

I AM BLACK
This is what you did to us.

I AM BLACK — YES I AM

I AM BLACK
Yes I am
I won't allow you to kneel on my neck.
I AM BLACK
Yes I am
We are no longer on your postcards with our
lifeless bodies hanging from a tree.

I AM BLACK
Why was I in chains? I was just a child.

I AM BLACK
Yes I am
I AM BLACK
I love my blackness
I AM BLACK!

I AM BLACK — YES I AM — THANK YOU

I AM BLACK
Yes I am
Thank you, Dr Martin Luther King Jr for giving us
The belief that we can have a dream.
I AM BLACK
Yes I am
Thank you to Claudette Colvin and Rosa Parks
I can sit anywhere on the bus.
I AM BLACK
Yes I am
Thank you, Harriet Tubman and Frederick Douglass,
for after all you went through, you saved so many from
slavery.

I AM BLACK — YES I AM — THANK YOU

I AM BLACK

Yes I am

Thank you, Sojourner Truth, you made history by showing us that,

even when times weren't on our side we can get justice.

I AM BLACK

Yes I am

Thank you, Ruby Bridges, for opening doors for us, defying segregation,

so that we could all go to school, be ourselves and get the same education.

I AM BLACK

Yes I am

Thank you, William Still, for conducting the Underground Railroad to free slaves.

I AM BLACK

Yes I am

Thank you, Nat Turner, for leading the only sustained rebellion and teaching the people, that slaves were not content with the lives bestowed upon them.

I AM BLACK — YES I AM — THANK YOU

I AM BLACK
Yes I am
Thank You, William Lloyd Garrison, as a white man to
stand up in those
Times. The founder of the American Anti-Slavery Society
and
the newspaper The Liberator, teaching the brutal and
honest truth and
promoting the emancipation of slaves.
I AM BLACK
Yes I am
Thank you, James McCune Smith, for showing us we are
more than slaves
and that no one can hold you back, as you went on to
become
the first black man to receive a medical degree.

I AM BLACK

Last and definitely not least, to George Floyd.
Thank you, you lost your life
And proved to the world that people of colour still
endure similar violence and oppression today
you have created a movement like never before. Your
death has inspired
life, we do matter.
Thank You to Darnella Frazier who captured the video
of the incident, as without you the world would have
never known.
RIP my brother. We will meet but on the other side.

**SMILE
AND
THE WORLD
WILL SMILE WITH YOU.**

Toni Morrison

Toni Morrison reshaped Literature and became the first black woman to win a Nobel Prize for Literature.

"There is no such thing as race.
None. There is just a human race —
scientifically, anthropologically.
Racism is a construct, a social construct and it has benefits.
Money can be made off of it, people who don't like themselves
can feel better because of it, it can describe certain kinds of
behaviour that are wrong or misleading,
so it has a social function, racism."

Phillis Wheatley

Phillis Wheatley was the first African-American author of a book of poetry. Born in West Africa, she was sold into slavery at the age of seven and transported to North America.

Hattie McDaniel

Hattie McDaniel was an American actress, singer-songwriter,
and comedian. She won the Academy Award for
Best Supporting Actress for her role as "Mammy"
in Gone with the Wind to become the first black

woman to win an Oscar.

Hattie was unable to attend the premiere of Gone with the Wind
in Atlanta because it was held at a whites-only theatre.
When she died in 1952, her final wish to be buried in Hollywood Cemetery was denied because the graveyard was restricted to whites only.

"I sincerely hope I shall always be a credit to my race and to the motion picture industry."

Ethel Waters

Ethel Waters was the first African-American to star on her own television show and the first African-American woman to be nominated for a Primetime Emmy Award.

John Baxter Taylor Jr

John Baxter Taylor Jr was an American track and field athlete,
notable as the first African-American to win an Olympic gold medal.

Cathay Williams

Cathay Williams an African-American soldier who enlisted in the United States Army under the pseudonym William Cathay. She was the first Black woman to enlist, and the only documented woman to serve in the United States Army posing as a man.

Matthew Henson

Matthew Henson was an American explorer who accompanied Robert Peary on seven voyages to the arctic spanning over 22 years,
and he may have been the first man,
black or white to reach the North Pole.

Robert Sengstacke Abbott

Robert Sengstacke Abbott founded The Chicago Defender with an investment of 25 cents. The newspaper soon became the most widely circulated black paper in the country making Robert one of the first black self-made millionaires.

Benjamin Banneker

Benjamin Banneker was one of the first black men to gain distinction in science. A mathematician and astronomer, Banneker saw astronomical patterns from which he could make calculations and predictions.

Dr Charles R. Drew

Dr Charles R. Drew was a pioneering black medical researcher and made ground-breaking discoveries in the storage and processing of blood for transfusions.

John Mercer Langston

John Mercer Langston was an American abolitionist, attorney, educator, activist, diplomat, and politician. An African-American, he became the first dean of the law school at Howard University and helped create the department. He was the first president of what is now Virginia State University, a historically black college.

Ella Josephine Baker

Ella Josephine Baker was a black civil rights and human rights activist. Whose career spanned five decades.

Garrett Augustus Morgan Sr

Garrett Augustus Morgan Sr was a black inventor, businessman and community leader. His most famous inventions were the three-position traffic signal and a smoke hood used in a 1916 tunnel construction disaster rescue.

Sarah Boone

Sarah Boone was a black inventor who made significant improvements to the ironing board. Sarah Boone's ironing board was designed to improve the quality of ironing sleeves and ladies' garments. She was one of four black lady inventors of her time.

Roger Arliner Young

Roger Arliner Young was an American scientist of zoology, biology, and marine biology. She was the first African-American woman to receive a Doctorate degree in zoology.

Percy Lavon Julian

Percy Lavon Julian was an American research chemist and a pioneer in the chemical synthesis of medicinal drugs from plants. His work laid the foundation for the steroid drug industry's production of cortisone, other corticosteroids, and birth control pills.

Rebecca Lee Crumpler

Rebecca Lee Crumpler became the first black woman to become a doctor of medicine in the United States.

Shirley Chisholm

Shirley Anita Chisholm was an American politician and became the first black lady to be elected to the United States congress.

Alice Ball

Alice Ball was an American chemist who developed the "Ball Method", the most effective treatment for leprosy during the early 20th century.

Edward Bouchet

Edward Bouchet was an American physicist and educator and was the first black man to earn a Ph.D. from any American university.

St. Elmo Brady

St. Elmo Brady was the first black man to obtain a Ph.D. degree in chemistry in the United States. He received his doctorate at the University of Illinois in 1916.

George Washington Carver

George Washington Carver was the most prominent black scientist of the 20th century, an agricultural scientist and inventor. A champion in crop rotation and educator of agricultural science.

Jesse Owens

Jesse Owens, the most famous athlete of his time. His performance at the 1936 Olympic Games captivated the world and got under the skin of the Nazis. Jesse Owens amazed the world with his talent, breaking world records and winning four gold medals.

Rosa Parks

Rosa Parks was a civil rights activist who refused to surrender her seat to a white passenger on a segregated bus; Rosa's defiance sparked the Montgomery Bus Boycott. Its success launched nationwide efforts to end racial segregation of public facilities.

Ernest Everett Just

Ernest Everett Just was an African-American biologist and educator best known for his pioneering work in the physiology of development, especially in fertilisation.

Marie Maynard Daly

Marie Maynard Daly was an American biochemist. Daly was the first black lady in the US to achieve a Ph.D. in chemistry.

Dr Martin Luther King Jr

Dr Martin Luther King Jr was an African-American minister and activist who became the most visible spokesperson and leader in the civil rights movement from 1955 until his assassination in 1968. King is best known for advancing civil rights through nonviolence and civil disobedience. His "I have a dream" speech that was heard by millions is still one of the most prolific speeches about change in racism and the divide between white and black to this day.

Harriet Tubman

Harriet Tubman escaped slavery and went on to save other enslaved people through the "Underground Railroad". Tubman is one of the most recognised icons in American history and her legacy has inspired countless people from every race and background.

Countee Cullen

Countee Cullen, Born Countee Leroy Porter, was an American poet, novelist, children's writer, and playwright, particularly well known during the Harlem Renaissance.

"Africa for Africans"

Martin Robinson Delany

Martin Robinson Delany was an African-American abolitionist, journalist, physician, soldier and writer, and arguably the first proponent of Black Nationalism.

Henry Louis Aaron

Better known as Hank Aaron. Aaron was an NL All Star for 20 seasons and an AL All-Star for one season, from 1955 through 1975. Aaron holds the record for the most All-Star Games selections.

Richard Allen

Richard Allen was a minister, educator, writer, and one of America's most active and influential black leaders. In 1794, he founded the African Methodist Episcopal Church, the first independent black denomination in the United States.

Marian Anderson

Marian Anderson was the first African-American to perform at the Metropolitan Opera in New York City on 7 January 1955. She participated in the civil rights movement in the 1960s, singing at the March on Washington for Jobs and Freedom in 1963.

Alicia Garza

Alicia Garza is an American civil rights activist and writer known for co-founding the international Black Lives Matter movement.

Crispus Attucks

Crispus Attucks was of African and Native American descent, widely regarded as the first person killed in the Boston Massacre and the first American killed in the American Revolution. He later became an icon of the anti-slavery movement in the 19th century, and supporters of the abolition movement praised him for playing a heroic role in the history of the United States.

Maya Angelou

Maya Angelou — born Marguerite Annie Johnson, was an American poet, memoirist, and civil rights activist. She published seven autobiographies, three books of essays, several books of poetry. She received dozens of awards and more than 50 honorary degrees.

"Hate, it has caused a lot of problems in the world, but has not solved one yet."

"I've learned that people will forget what you said, people will forget what you did, but people will never forget how you made them feel."

James Arthur Baldwin

James Arthur Baldwin was an American novelist, playwright, essayist, poet, and activist. His essays explore intricacies of racial, sexual, and class distinctions in Western society.

Mary Jane McLeod Bethune

Mary Jane McLeod Bethune founded the National Council for Negro Women in 1935. Appointed as a national adviser to President Franklin D. Roosevelt, whom she worked with to create the Federal Council on Negro Affairs, also known as the Black Cabinet. She was known as "The First Lady of The Struggle" because of her commitment to gain better lives for African- Americans.

Hiram Rhodes Revels

Hiram Rhodes Revels was a Republican US Senator, Minister in the African Methodist Episcopal Church, and a college administrator.

Guion Bluford

Guion Bluford was a decorated Air Force pilot in Vietnam before joining NASA in the late 1970s. In 1983, he became the first African-American to travel into space when he served as a mission specialist aboard the space shuttle Challenger.

Gwendolyn Elizabeth Brooks

Gwendolyn Elizabeth Brooks was a black poet, author, and teacher from the US. Her work often dealt with the personal celebrations and struggles of ordinary people in her community.

"When you use the term minority or minorities in reference to people, you're telling them that they're less than somebody else."

John William Coltrane

John William Coltrane was an American jazz saxophonist and composer and a pioneer in his field. He was the face of free jazz and became an inspiration to many.

Ralph Johnson Bunche

Ralph Johnson Bunche was a black American political scientist, academic, and diplomat who received the 1950 Nobel Peace Prize for his late 1940s mediation in Israel. In 1963, he was awarded the Presidential Medal of Freedom by President John F. Kennedy.

William Edward Burkhart Du Bois

(February 23, 1868 – August 27, 1963)
I AM BLACK
Socialist and Historian

Paul Laurence Dunbar

Paul Laurence Dunbar was born on June 27, 1872 to freed slaves from Kentucky. He became one of the first influential black poets in American literature.

"We wear the mask that grins and lies, it hides our cheeks and shades our eyes—this debt we pay to human guile; with torn and bleeding hearts we smile"

Katherine Mary Dunham

Katherine Mary Dunham was an African-American dancer, choreographer, author, educator, anthropologist and social activist. She has been called the "matriarch and queen mother of black dance".

Edward Kennedy "Duke" Ellington

(April 29, 1899 – May 24, 1974)
I AM BLACK
Composer, Pianist and Leader of a Jazz Orchestra

John Hope Franklin

(January 2, 1915 – March 25, 2009)
I AM BLACK
Historian of the United States

Henry Highland Garnet

(December 23, 1815 – February 13, 1882)
I AM BLACK
Abolitionist Minister who escaped from slavery

Marcus Mosiah Garvey Jr

(17 August, 1887 – 10 June, 1940)
I AM BLACK
Published Activist, Entrepreneur

Dorothy Irene Height

Dorothy Irene Height was a leader in addressing the rights of both women and African-Americans as the President of the National Council of Negro Women.

Prince Hall

Prince Hall was an abolitionist and leader in the free black community in Boston. He founded Prince Hall Freemasonry and pushed for education rights for African-American children.

Fannie Lou Hamer

Fannie Lou Hamer was an American voting and women's rights activist, community organiser, and a leader in the civil rights movement. She was the co-founder and vice-chair of the Freedom Democratic Party.

"I am sick and tired of being sick and tired.

Lorraine Vivian Hansberry

(May 19, 1930 – January 12, 1965)
An American playwright whose "A Raisin in the sun" was the first drama by an African — American woman to be produced on Broadway.

Charles Hamilton Houston

(September 3, 1895 – April 22, 1950)
I AM BLACK
A Black lawyer who played a major role in tearing apart the Jim Crow laws and was a part of training the future Supreme Court justice Thurgood Marshall

Zora Neale Hurston

(January 7, 1891 – January 28, 1960)
Author and film maker, Novel – Their eyes were watching God 1937

Mae Carol Jemison

(born October 17, 1956)
I AM BLACK
First Black woman to travel into space

Jesse Jackson

(born October 8, 1941)
I AM BLACK
Baptist Minister and Politician

James Weldon Johnson

(June 17, 1871 – June 26, 1938)
I AM BLACK
Writer and Civil Rights Activist

John Arthur Johnson

(March 31, 1878 – June 10, 1946)
The first African- American world heavyweight boxing champion, and regarded as one of the most influential boxers of all time

John Harold Johnson

(January 19, 1918 – August 8, 2005)
I AM BLACK
Businessman and Publisher

Maulana Ndabezitha Karenga, previously known as Ron Karenga, Ronald McKinley Everett.

I AM BLACK
African-American professor of Africana studies, activist and author. He was active in the Black Power movement in the 60s and 70s.

Alain Leroy Locke

(September 13, 1885 – June 9, 1954)
I AM BLACK
A philosophical architect.

Mary Edmonia Lewis, "Wildfire"

(July 4, 1844 – September 17, 1907)
I AM BLACK
Born Free she became the first African – American sculptor to attain national and international distinction

Joseph Louis Barrow

(May 13, 1914 – April 12, 1981)
I AM BLACK
Professional Boxer, one of the greatest heavyweight boxers of all time.

Benjamin Elijah Mays

(August 1, 1894 – March 28, 1984)
I AM BLACK
A civil rights leader credited with laying the intellectual foundations.

Festus Claudius "Claude" McKay

(September 15, 1889 – May 22, 1948)
I AM BLACK
A Jamaican Writer and Poet.

Elijah J. McCoy

(May 2, 1844 – October 10, 1929)
I AM BLACK
An Inventor and Engineer, I had 57 US patents for the lubrication of the steam engines.

Doris "Dorie" Miller

(October 12, 1919 – November 24, 1943)
I AM BLACK
Manned anti-aircraft guns during the attack on Pearl
Harbour 7/12/1941

Oscar Devereaux Micheaux

(January 2, 1884 – March 25, 1951)
I AM BLACK
Film director and independent producer

Adam Clayton Powell Jr

(November 29, 1908 – April 4, 1972)
I AM BLACK
A Pastor and a Politician

Elijah Muhammad
(born Elijah Robert Poole)

(October 7, 1897 – February 25, 1975)
I AM BLACK
A religious leader who led the nation of Islam.

Muhammad Ali, born Cassius Marcellus Clay Jr

(January 17, 1942 – June 3, 2016)
I AM BLACK
Professional Boxer and Activist

Asa Philip Randolph

(April 15, 1889 – May 16, 1979)
I AM BLACK
An American Labour Unionist, Civil Rights Activist and a Social Politician

Medgar Wiley Evers

(July 2, 1925 – June 12, 1963)
I AM BLACK
Civil Rights Activist, World War Two Veteran

James Howard Meredith

(born June 25, 1933)
I AM BLACK
Political Adviser and Air Veteran

Emmett Louis Till

(July 25, 1941 – August 28, 1955)
I AM BLACK
He was 14 years old and lynched, after being accused of offending a white woman.

Thurgood Marshall

(July 2, 1908 – January 24, 1993)
I AM BLACK
American Lawyer working in the Clinton White House

Malcolm X

El-Hajj Malik El-Shabazz born Malcolm Little, better known as Malcolm X, was an African-American minister and human rights activist who was a popular figure during the civil rights movement.

I AM BLACK

As I look at all the quotes from myself and all of these black influential people some of whom I never read or even heard about, it saddens me to the core. We as black people never wanted to be hated for our colour, why the hell are we anyway? Anything we do we are questioned for it, we can do films with an all-black cast and we are questioned for it, yet we never question anyone, "why do you want a black-owned shop?" yet we never questioned you. Why on earth are we asked these things when all along you have been doing the very same for as long as I have lived, why is it different for us?

Another thing, what gives you the right to touch my hair or to question what I do with it? It's just hair, a little different from yours, but still hair. I hear you chatting about it, even friends that I used to work with. My work team now are simply the best and all white. I am the only black person to work where I do. My team and I are one; we have mutual respect for each other.

I will say, yes, I have encountered racism as I have got older, but I will not take that bigotry. If you hate me because of my colour, then that's a problem you need to deal with and deal with it you shall. I will treat you the way my mother brought me up, to respect and be kind to all. Try it; it's easy.

I mean, you hate me because I am black, talented, I may be even pretty but most of all you hate me because I am me and I shine in the way you don't. If you just open your heart and get rid of all the bitterness, you will shine too. Come and get to know me; don't let my colour define who I am and who you are. It's just skin. I have so many white beautiful friends, and black too.

People of all races, we are all human beings. Love Everyone. Simple. Always be kind.

Smile and the world will smile with you.

T xx

I have a dream

I can just about see it, in the dark clouds that still surround me. I'll kiss in the wind and all this hatred will be gone, I wish.

We just don't need it, leave it behind, and just be kind.

I am neither above nor beneath you.

I was born this way, I didn't expect my colour to offend anyone, I came out crying like every other baby, I didn't think we were different as I was just a baby, just a baby who couldn't see, never mind see colour and why should that even matter? Look at the rainbow; it has many colours and it's so beautiful; we should all shine in the sun as one.

Let's just share it, equally, as we are all equal.

Stop all the hate, I love you, just love me as I am, I'm not only black, I'm a being, yes I am, I am a human being.

Love will always win in the end because without love what else do we really have?

Sprinkle your kindness and love everywhere; it would be a game changer for us all.

We all have a place in this world.

That's it! That's all! That is all!

My Beautiful Mum

Mummy, I could never have left you out of my first book; living without you is the worst pain I have endured.

You were and always will be my inspiration. I really never encountered racism as you shielded myself and my siblings from it; it was only when Roots came on the TV we knew.

Thank You, Mum, for everything you did for me I will cherish and love you for eternity.

To Arci
love of love
TRISH CARESS